Jen and Max

By Milliana Rosa
Illustrated by Nan Brooks

Target Skill *Review*
High-Frequency Words *Review*

PEARSON
Scott Foresman

Jen and Max are six.

They are big kids.

Jen can zip.

Max can run.

They like to zip and run.

Mom and Dad have a box.

It is a big red box.

It is a gift.

What is in the box, Mom?

It is a gift for you and Max.

Jen and Max look at the box.
They look in the big red box.

Look! Jen and Max see a cat.

It is Tag, the little cat.

Tag is little and soft.

Jen and Max like Tag.

Tag likes Jen and Max.